No Nonsense Number

Activities to support learning in Years 6 and 7

Part A

Suzi de Gouveia,
Jackie Andrews
and Jude Callaghan

essential
resources

Title:	No Nonsense Number Activities to support learning in Years 6 and 7 – Part A
Authors:	Suzi de Gouveia, Jackie Andrews and Jude Callaghan
Editor:	Tanya Tremewan
Book code:	293A
ISBN:	978-1-877523-04-5
Published:	2009
Publisher:	Essential Resources Educational Publishers Limited

United Kingdom:	**Australia:**	**New Zealand:**
Unit 8–10 Parkside	PO Box 90	PO Box 5036
Shortgate Lane	Oak Flats	Invercargill
Laughton, BN8 6DG	NSW 2529	
ph: 0845 3636 147	ph: 1800 005 068	ph: 0800 087 376
fax: 0845 3636 148	fax: 1800 981 213	fax: 0800 937 825

Website:	www.essentialresourcesuk.com
Copyright:	Text: © Suzi de Gouveia, Jackie Andrews and Jude Callaghan, 2009 Edition and Illustrations: © Essential Resources Educational Publishers Limited, 2009

About the authors: Suzi is the enthusiastic headteacher of St Teresa's Primary School in Christchurch, New Zealand. She has international teaching experience and has had the pleasure of teaching in a multi-cultural environment. Over 20 years of teaching have enabled Suzi to develop a wealth of ideas and resources to best help children.

Jackie is an experienced teacher who has taught primary children in both New Zealand and the United Kingdom. As a mother of three young children she is taking time out of the classroom and is enjoying having the time to diversify.

Jude is an experienced, enthusiastic teacher with a passion for teaching and learning. Her teaching programmes are innovative and exciting. She has joined the No Nonsense Number writing team to share her deep understanding and wealth of ideas.

Contents

Introduction

This book forms part of the *No Nonsense Number* Series that supports Learning in Years 6 and 7.

Pupil templates have been included as a way reinforcing selected specific learning objectives. For each of these templates, children develop their own problems for other pupils to solve.

Answers to the problems are provided at the end of this book. Unless otherwise specified, the fractions have not been simplified. However, you may choose to encourage your pupils to do this.

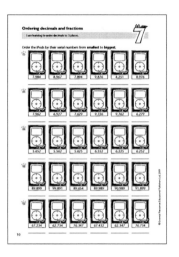

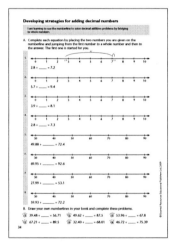

Curriculum Links

Strand	Learning objectives *Most children learn to:*
Year 6	
Counting and understanding number	• use decimal notation for tenths, hundredths and thousandths; partition, round and order decimals with up to three places, and position them on the number line. • express a larger whole number as a fraction of a smaller one (e.g. recognise that 8 slices of a 5-slice pizza represents 8/5 or 13/5 pizzas); simplify fractions by cancelling common factors
Calculating	• Calculate mentally with integers and decimals: U.t ± U.t

Source: Adapted from *The Primary Framework for Mathematics*, 2006

© Essential Resources Educational Publishers Ltd, 2009

Skip-counting in decimals and fractions

I am learning to skip-count in hundredths.

Fill in the missing numbers. Count on in hundredths. The first one is started for you.

1. 27.692 | 27.702
2. 1.909
3. 89.383
4. 61.194
5. 2.42
6. 17.605
7. 46.27
8. 38.516

Fill in the missing numbers. Count back in hundredths. The first one is started for you.

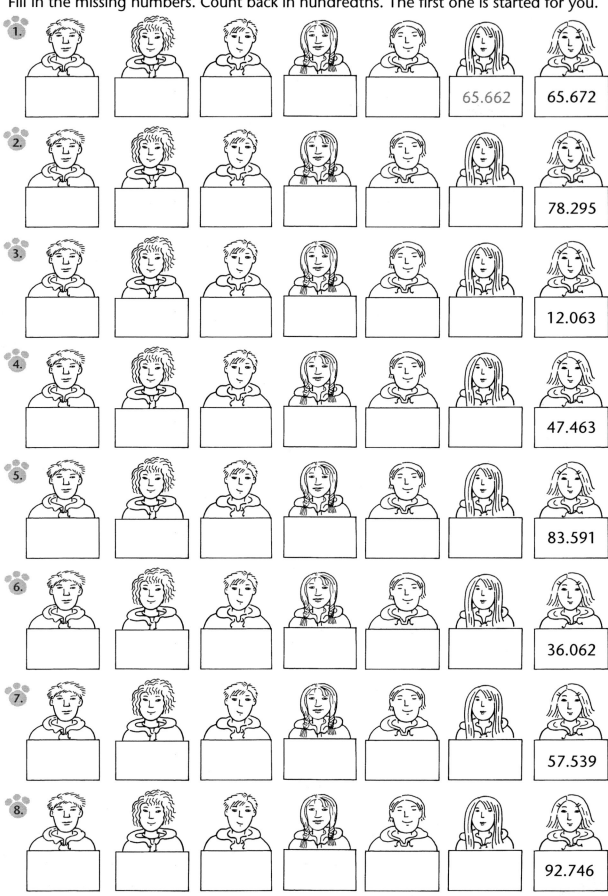

1. 65.662 65.672

2. 78.295

3. 12.063

4. 47.463

5. 83.591

6. 36.062

7. 57.539

8. 92.746

Fill in the missing numbers. Count on in thousandths. The first one is started for you.

1. 16.860   16.861

2. 63.306

3. 98.791

4. 31.943

5. 57.459

6. 84.618

7. 52.175

8. 40.527

Fill in the missing numbers. Count back in thousandths. The first one is started for you.

1. [ ] [ ] [ ] [ ] [ ] 45.137 45.138

2. [ ] [ ] [ ] [ ] [ ] [ ] 37.425

3. [ ] [ ] [ ] [ ] [ ] [ ] 90.704

4. [ ] [ ] [ ] [ ] [ ] [ ] 78.659

5. [ ] [ ] [ ] [ ] [ ] [ ] 82.342

6. [ ] [ ] [ ] [ ] [ ] [ ] 23.689

7. [ ] [ ] [ ] [ ] [ ] [ ] 64.563

8. [ ] [ ] [ ] [ ] [ ] [ ] 56.876

Fill in the missing numbers on the numberline.

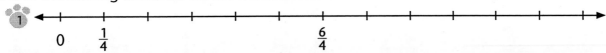

0    $\frac{1}{4}$ $\frac{6}{4}$

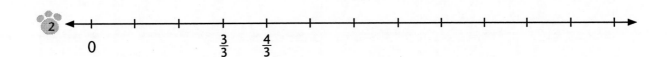

0                    $\frac{3}{3}$ $\frac{4}{3}$

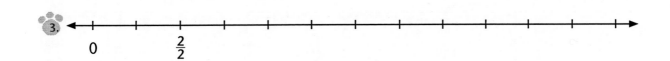

0              $\frac{2}{2}$

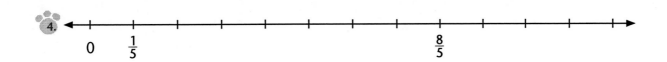

0    $\frac{1}{5}$ $\frac{8}{5}$

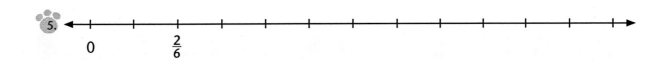

0              $\frac{2}{6}$

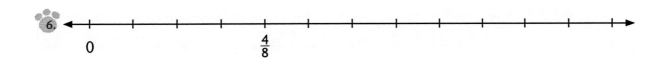

0                        $\frac{4}{8}$

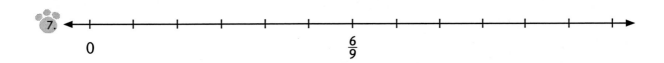

0                                      $\frac{6}{9}$

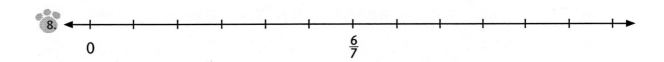

0                                      $\frac{6}{7}$

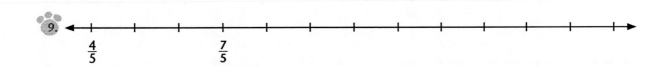

$\frac{4}{5}$ $\frac{7}{5}$

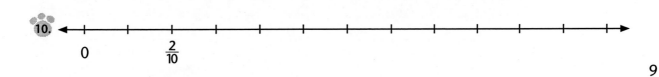

0              $\frac{2}{10}$

Ordering decimals and fractions

I am learning to order decimals to 3 places.

Order the iPods by their serial numbers from **smallest** to **biggest**.

1. 7.984 | 8.967 | 7.894 | 9.876 | 4.251 | 8.976

2. 7.962 | 6.927 | 7.629 | 9.726 | 9.762 | 6.279

3. 5.652 | 5.562 | 5.625 | 6.552 | 6.225 | 6.252

4. 89.899 | 99.891 | 89.654 | 89.989 | 90.989 | 91.899

5. 67.234 | 62.734 | 76.347 | 67.432 | 62.347 | 76.734

10

© Essential Resources Educational Publishers Ltd, 2009

Order the mobile phones by their serial numbers from **biggest** to **smallest**.

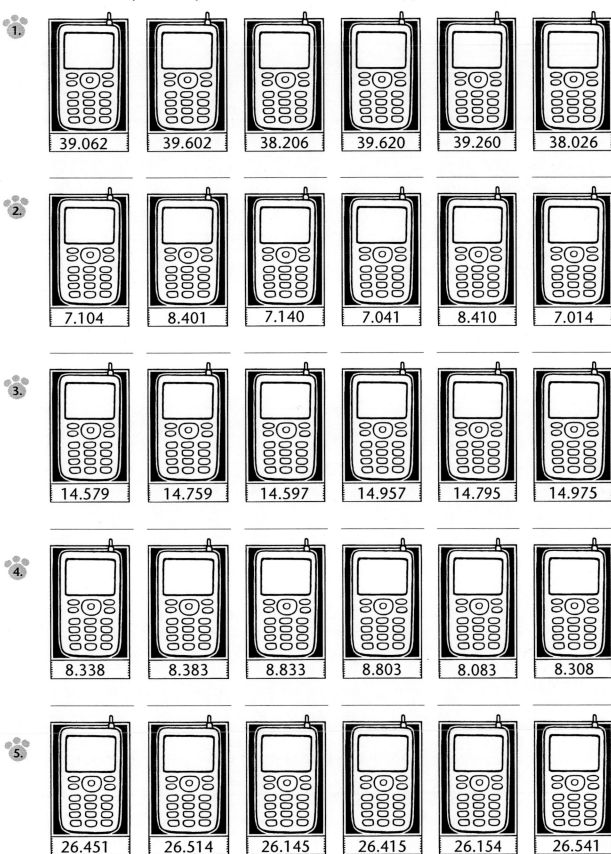

1. 39.062 39.602 38.206 39.620 39.260 38.026

2. 7.104 8.401 7.140 7.041 8.410 7.014

3. 14.579 14.759 14.597 14.957 14.795 14.975

4. 8.338 8.383 8.833 8.803 8.083 8.308

5. 26.451 26.514 26.145 26.415 26.154 26.541

1. Divide the strip into halves. Colour $\frac{1}{2}$.

2. Divide the strip into sixths. Colour $\frac{1}{6}$.

3. Divide the strip into quarters. Colour $\frac{1}{4}$.

4. Divide the strip into sevenths. Colour $\frac{1}{7}$.

5. Divide the strip into ninths. Colour $\frac{1}{9}$.

6. Divide the strip into fifths. Colour $\frac{1}{5}$.

7. Divide the strip into tenths. Colour $\frac{1}{10}$.

8. Divide the strip into eighths. Colour $\frac{1}{8}$.

9. Divide the strip into thirds. Colour $\frac{1}{3}$.

10. Order these numbers from **smallest** to **biggest** and then write the rule that explains this order.

$$1 \quad \frac{1}{9} \quad \frac{1}{4} \quad \frac{1}{2} \quad \frac{1}{10} \quad \frac{1}{3} \quad \frac{1}{5} \quad \frac{1}{6} \quad \frac{1}{8} \quad \frac{1}{7}$$

____ ____ ____ ____ ____ ____ ____ ____ ____ ____

_____

Identifying place value

I am learning to identify place value.

Write the value of the underlined digit. The first one is done for you.

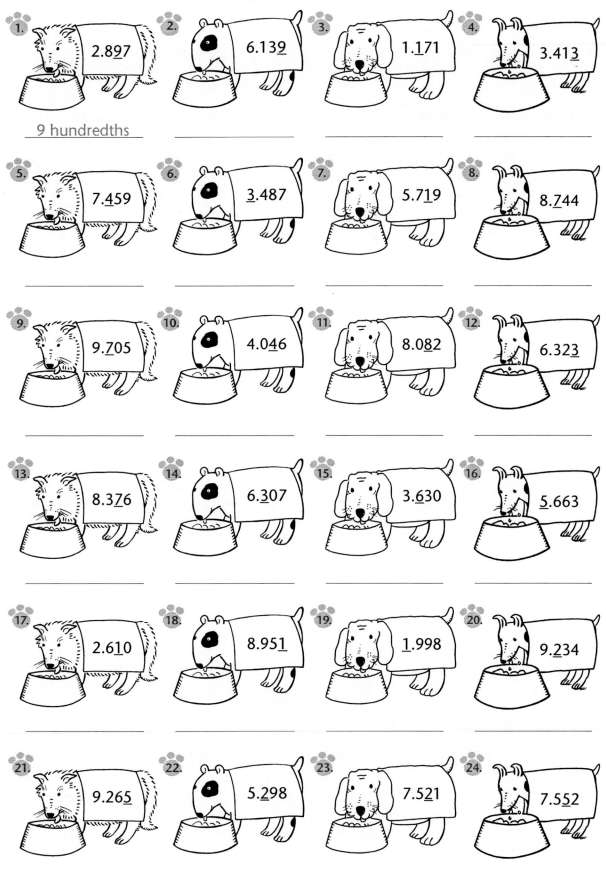

1. 2.8<u>9</u>7
     9 hundredths

2. 6.13<u>9</u>

3. 1.<u>1</u>71

4. 3.41<u>3</u>

5. 7.<u>4</u>59

6. <u>3</u>.487

7. 5.7<u>1</u>9

8. 8.<u>7</u>44

9. 9.<u>7</u>05

10. 4.0<u>4</u>6

11. 8.0<u>8</u>2

12. 6.32<u>3</u>

13. 8.3<u>7</u>6

14. 6.<u>3</u>07

15. 3.<u>6</u>30

16. <u>5</u>.663

17. 2.6<u>1</u>0

18. 8.95<u>1</u>

19. <u>1</u>.998

20. 9.<u>2</u>34

21. 9.26<u>5</u>

22. 5.<u>2</u>98

23. 7.5<u>2</u>1

24. 7.5<u>5</u>2

A. What is the value of the digit **6** in each of these numbers?

  1. 604.721   2. 349.065   3. 106.47   4. 7.896   5. 68.720

_____   _____   _____   _____   _____

B. What is the value of the digit **5** in each of these numbers?

  1. 62.051   2. 45.839   3. 72.514   4. 508.13   5. 12.305

_____   _____   _____   _____   _____

C. What is the value of the digit **7** in each of these numbers?

  1. 428.716   2. 64.2871   3. 287.146   4. 94.367   5. 723.984

_____   _____   _____   _____   _____

D. What is the value of the digit **8** in each of these numbers?

  1. 964.08   2. 179.861   3. 410.285   4. 38.392   5. 845.762

_____   _____   _____   _____   _____

  6. 302.87   7. 318.027   8. 861.727   9. 95.841   10. 260.948

_____   _____   _____   _____   _____

E. In which column is the digit **9** in each of these numbers?

  1. 56 329.417   2. 89 654.213   3. 569 234.36   4. 964 381.562

_____   _____   _____   _____

F. Write 4 four-digit numbers in which the digit **2** has the value of **2 hundredths**.

_____   _____   _____   _____

G. Write 4 four-digit numbers in which the digit **9** has the value of **9 tenths**.

_____   _____   _____   _____

H. Write 4 four-digit numbers in which the digit **6** has the value of **6 thousandths**.

_____   _____   _____   _____

© Essential Resources Educational Publishers Ltd, 2009

Write the numbers on each caterpillar in expanded form. The first one is done for you.

1. 6 · 7 9 1   6 + 0.7 + 0.09 + 0.001

2. 1 · 2 6 3 _____

3. 4 · 1 7 2 _____

4. 7 · 5 9 7 _____

5. 5 · 2 7 4 _____

6. 2 · 4 1 8 _____

7. 6 · 0 8 3 _____

8. 7 · 3 2 1 _____

9. 6 · 8 2 6 _____

10. 9 · 4 1 5 _____

11. 1 · 1 5 0 _____

12. 3 · 9 0 6 _____

13. 5 · 0 6 4 _____

14. 2 · 5 9 9 _____

15. 4 · 7 3 8 _____

16. 8 · 3 8 5 _____

I am learning to identify place value with whole numbers and decimals.

Write each decimal number in expanded form. The first one is done for you.

		Ones	Tenths	Hundredths	Thousandths
1.	2.093	2	0.0	0.09	0.003
2.	8.802				
3.	4.568				
4.	3.114				
5.	7.982				
6.	4.671				
7.	9.205				
8.	6.073				
9.	5.166				
10.	1.324				
11.	4.789				
12.	6.157				
13.	1.499				
14.	6.236				
15.	3.848				
16.	5.515				
17.	7.339				
18.	5.946				
19.	2.620				
20.	8.458				
21.	1.021				
22.	9.717				
23.	4.294				
24.	6.905				

Moving between compact and expanded forms

I am learning to rename whole numbers and decimals in compact form.

A. Write these number sentences in compact form.

1. 26 + 0.5 + 0.03 + 0.009 _____
2. 19 + 0.9 + 0.08 + 0.002 _____
3. 87 + 0.9 + 0.004 _____
4. 36 + 0.5 + 0.06 + 0.005 _____
5. 74 + 0.06 + 0.008 _____

6. 36 + 0.6 + 0.09 + 0.002 _____
7. 21 + 0.5 + 0.007 _____
8. 85 + 0.1 + 0.09 + 0.002 _____
9. 66 + 0.07 + 0.003 _____
10. 54 + 0.1 + 0.09 + 0.005 _____

B. Write these numbers in compact form.

1. 4 ones   6 tenths   8 hundredths   9 thousandths _____
2. 8 ones   9 tenths   0 hundredths   4 thousandths _____
3. 3 ones   5 tenths   6 hundredths   3 thousandths _____
4. 7 ones   0 tenths   8 hundredths   5 thousandths _____
5. 5 ones   3 tenths   4 hundredths   0 thousandths _____

C. Complete the table. The first row is done for you.

	00.000	00.000	00.000	00.000	00.000	Compact
1.	5	3	3	6	8	53.368
2.	8	9	2	7	9	
3.	4	2	9	5	4	
4.	2	7	0	0	3	
5.	4	8	3	5	7	
6.	1	1	7	0	4	
7.	7	0	9	4	9	
8.	6	5	8	0	0	
9.	2	1	6	1	6	
10.	3	7	8	5	2	
11.	6	8	4	5	7	

Write the number in expanded form. The first one is done for you.

#	Number	Expanded form
1.	31.915	30 + 1 + 0.9 + 0.01 + 0.005
2.	106.051	
3.	91.743	
4.	898.544	
5.	72.105	
6.	80.638	
7.	122.497	
8.	101.509	
9.	15.313	
10.	383.089	
11.	470.996	
12.	29.271	
13.	942.323	
14.	47.828	
15.	34.082	
16.	53.174	
17.	48.767	
18.	65.652	
19.	59.286	
20.	74.834	
21.	66.951	
22.	117.462	
23.	65.297	
24.	1.267	
25.	879.346	

Making groupings of 10, 100 and 1000

I am learning the groupings of 10, 100 and 1 000 that can be made from a number.

A. How many groups of 10, 100 and 1 000 can be made from each of these numbers?

		Tens	Hundreds	Thousands
1.	372 203			
2.	84 758			
3.	49 394			
4.	1 786 327			
5.	25 051			
6.	23 845			
7.	601 676			
8.	56 982			
9.	1 940 673			
10.	548 321			

B. Match the playstation console with its screen to show the correct amount of hundreds in each number.

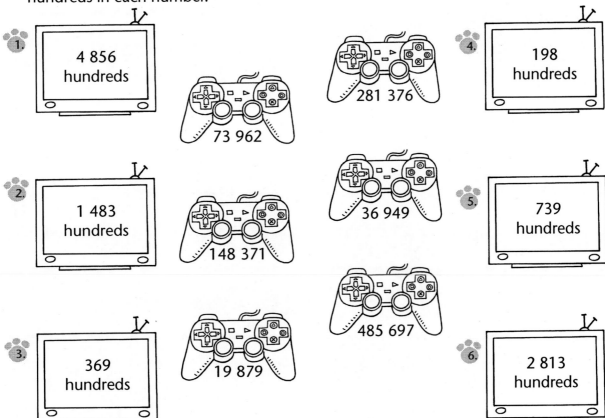

1. 4 856 hundreds

73 962

281 376

4. 198 hundreds

2. 1 483 hundreds

148 371

36 949

5. 739 hundreds

3. 369 hundreds

19 879

485 697

6. 2 813 hundreds

I am learning the groupings of 10, 100 and 1 000 that can be made from a number.

A. How many groups of 10, 100 and 1 000 can be made from each of these numbers?

		Tens	Hundreds	Thousands
1.	54 962			
2.	365 782			
3.	458 794			
4.	123 154			
5.	720 204			
6.	832 451			
7.	4 962 093			
8.	4 539 281			
9.	6 230 746			
10.	8 146 023			

B. Match the playstation console with its screen to show the correct amount of thousands in each number.

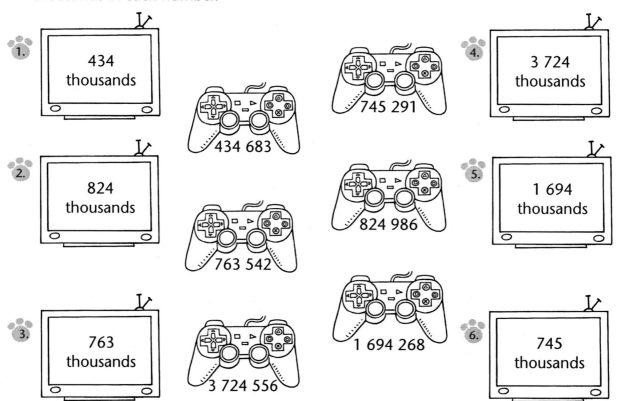

1. 434 thousands

434 683

745 291

4. 3 724 thousands

2. 824 thousands

763 542

824 986

5. 1 694 thousands

3. 763 thousands

3 724 556

1 694 268

6. 745 thousands

20

Converting improper fractions

I am learning to convert an improper fraction to a mixed number.

Match the improper fraction to the unifix blocks. Write the number as a mixed number. The first one is done for you.

#	Fraction	Blocks		Mixed number
1.	$\dfrac{7}{4}$		$\longrightarrow$	
2.	$\dfrac{7}{3}$		$\longrightarrow$	
3.	$\dfrac{12}{6}$		$\longrightarrow$	$1\dfrac{3}{4}$
4.	$\dfrac{19}{10}$		$\longrightarrow$	
5.	$\dfrac{5}{2}$		$\longrightarrow$	
6.	$\dfrac{12}{5}$		$\longrightarrow$	
7.	$\dfrac{12}{8}$		$\longrightarrow$	
8.	$\dfrac{5}{3}$		$\longrightarrow$	

I am learning to convert an improper fraction to a mixed number.

Match the improper fraction to the unifix blocks. Write the number as a mixed number.

1. $\dfrac{4}{2}$ 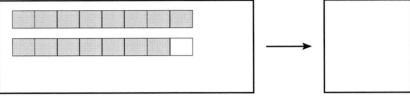 →

2. $\dfrac{15}{8}$  →

3. $\dfrac{6}{5}$  → **2**

4. $\dfrac{8}{3}$ 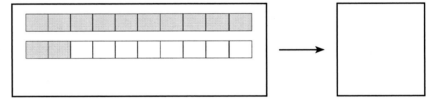 →

5. $\dfrac{4}{3}$  →

6. $\dfrac{12}{10}$  →

7. $\dfrac{8}{5}$  →

8. $\dfrac{11}{4}$ →

I am learning to convert an improper fraction to a mixed number.

Write some improper fractions in the left-hand boxes. Draw what unifix blocks would look like in the middle boxes. Give the sheet to a partner to complete.
Match the improper fraction to the unifix blocks. Write the number as a mixed number.

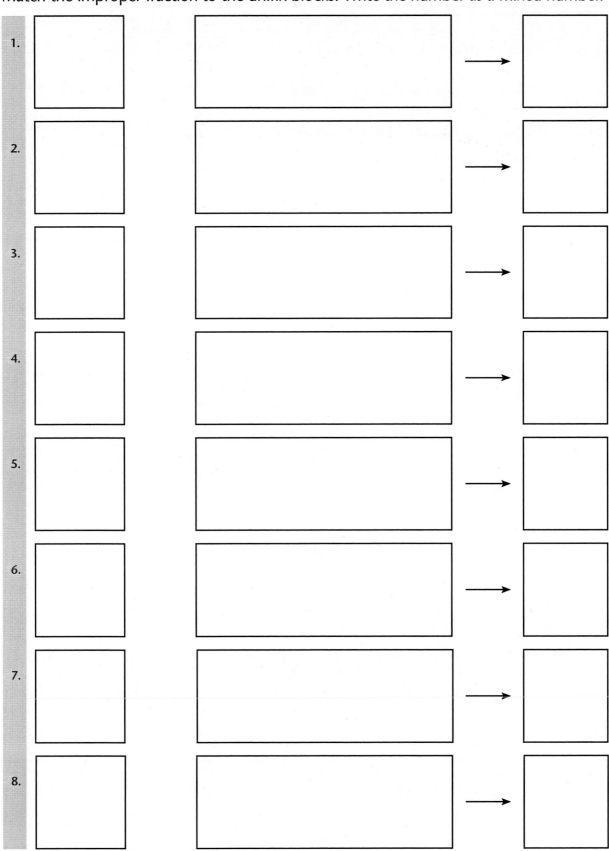

Learning equivalent fractions

I am learning equivalent fractions for halves, quarters, thirds, fifths and tenths.

Colour all the fractions equivalent to $\frac{3}{5}$ in red.

Colour all the fractions equivalent to $\frac{1}{2}$ in green.

Colour all the fractions equivalent to $\frac{3}{4}$ in purple.

Colour all the fractions equivalent to $\frac{8}{10}$ in orange.

Colour all the fractions equivalent to $\frac{2}{3}$ in yellow.

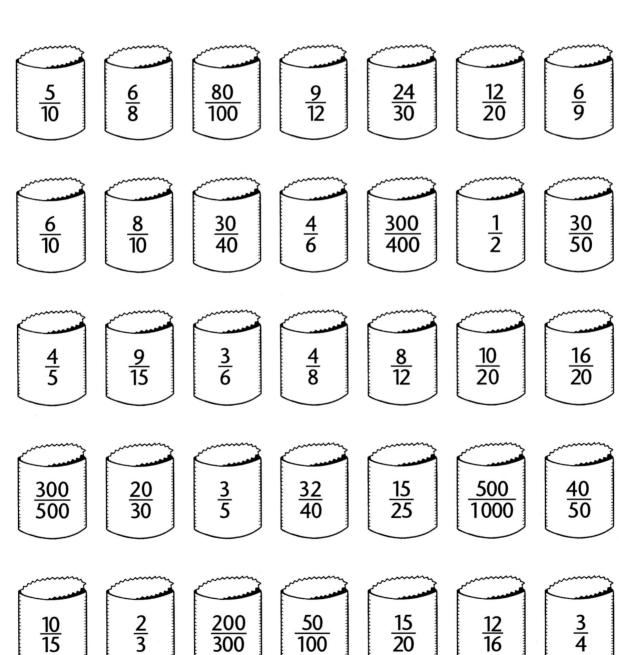

| $\frac{5}{10}$ | $\frac{6}{8}$ | $\frac{80}{100}$ | $\frac{9}{12}$ | $\frac{24}{30}$ | $\frac{12}{20}$ | $\frac{6}{9}$ |

| $\frac{6}{10}$ | $\frac{8}{10}$ | $\frac{30}{40}$ | $\frac{4}{6}$ | $\frac{300}{400}$ | $\frac{1}{2}$ | $\frac{30}{50}$ |

| $\frac{4}{5}$ | $\frac{9}{15}$ | $\frac{3}{6}$ | $\frac{4}{8}$ | $\frac{8}{12}$ | $\frac{10}{20}$ | $\frac{16}{20}$ |

| $\frac{300}{500}$ | $\frac{20}{30}$ | $\frac{3}{5}$ | $\frac{32}{40}$ | $\frac{15}{25}$ | $\frac{500}{1000}$ | $\frac{40}{50}$ |

| $\frac{10}{15}$ | $\frac{2}{3}$ | $\frac{200}{300}$ | $\frac{50}{100}$ | $\frac{15}{20}$ | $\frac{12}{16}$ | $\frac{3}{4}$ |

I am learning equivalent fractions for halves, quarters, fifths and tenths.

Colour all the fractions equivalent to $\frac{1}{2}$ in red.

Colour all the fractions equivalent to $\frac{1}{10}$ in green.

Colour all the fractions equivalent to $\frac{2}{5}$ in purple.

Colour all the fractions equivalent to $\frac{1}{5}$ in orange.

Colour all the fractions equivalent to $\frac{1}{4}$ in yellow.

Colour all the fractions equivalent to $\frac{3}{4}$ in blue.

Colour all the fractions equivalent to $\frac{3}{5}$ in brown.

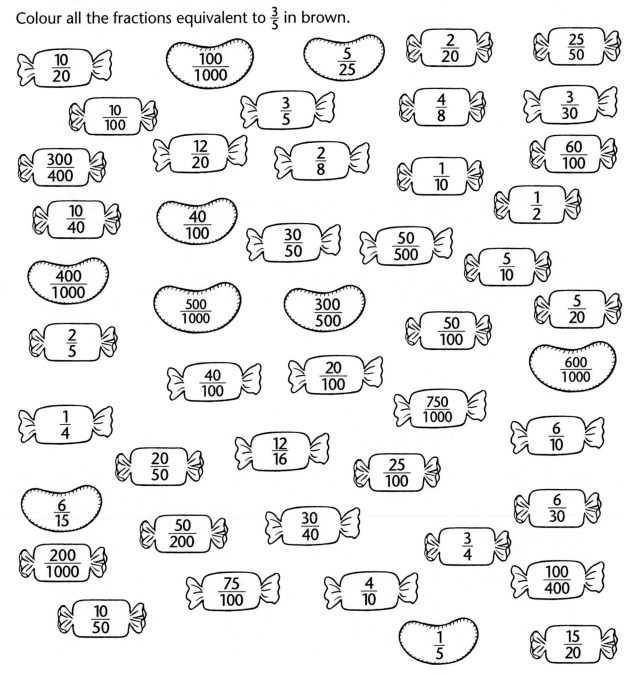

25

Matthew took his friends to The Pizza Place for his birthday treat. Match the friends who ate the same amount as each other.

1. I have eaten $\frac{1}{2}$ of a pizza.

I have eaten $\frac{8}{8}$ of a pizza.

2. I have eaten $\frac{2}{3}$ of a pizza.

I have eaten $\frac{4}{6}$ of a pizza.

3. I have eaten 1 pizza.

I have eaten $\frac{4}{8}$ of a pizza.

4. I have eaten $\frac{3}{4}$ of a pizza.

I have eaten $\frac{8}{20}$ of a pizza.

5. I have eaten $\frac{2}{5}$ of a pizza.

I have eaten $\frac{10}{12}$ of a pizza.

6. I have eaten $\frac{5}{6}$ of a pizza.

I have eaten $\frac{15}{20}$ of a pizza.

Rounding decimal numbers

I am learning to round decimals to the nearest whole number.

Round each number to the nearest whole number.

1.
4.37

_____

2.
27.80

_____

3.
30.23

_____

4.
16.92

_____

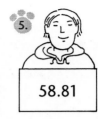
5.
58.81

_____

6.
73.4

_____

7.
69.48

_____

8.
135.29

_____

9.
28.81

_____

10.
57.65

_____

11.
40.10

_____

12.
84.9

_____

13.
3.16

_____

14.
8.96

_____

15.
6.19

_____

16.
12.74

_____

17.
7.39

_____

18.
6.13

_____

19.
14.57

_____

20.
7.74

_____

21.
49.0

_____

22.
9.57

_____

23.
25.2

_____

24.
7.59

_____

25.
5.65

_____

26.
3.03

_____

27.
23.12

_____

28.
6.46

_____

29.
8.08

_____

30.
9.84

_____

Round each number to the nearest tenth.

1. 16.13

2. 54.17

3. 65.76

4. 49.09

5. 72.36

6. 31.61

7. 35.91

8. 21.28

9. 69.26

10. 91.47

11. 49.97

12. 91.53

13. 69.72

14. 16.17

15. 27.15

16. 54.26

17. 63.81

18. 72.96

19. 96.85

20. 61.62

21. 59.47

22. 64.78

23. 72.69

24. 85.69

25. 72.38

26. 72.89

27. 65.55

28. 54.98

29. 70.95

30. 83.27

I am learning to round decimals to the nearest whole number and the nearest tenth.

Round the number on each bird to the nearest whole number and the nearest tenth.

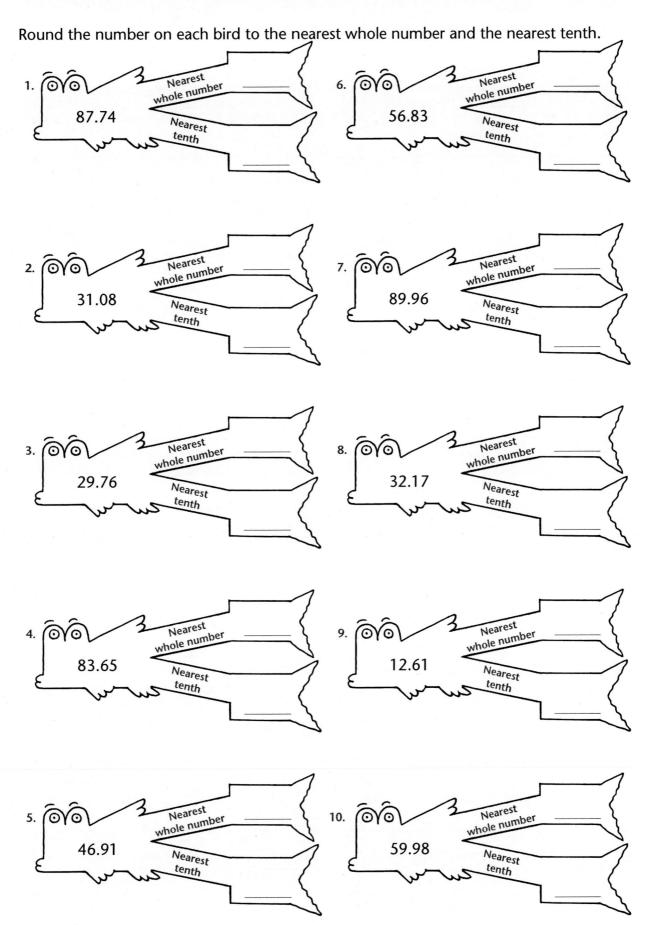

1. 87.74
Nearest whole number _____
Nearest tenth _____

2. 31.08
Nearest whole number _____
Nearest tenth _____

3. 29.76
Nearest whole number _____
Nearest tenth _____

4. 83.65
Nearest whole number _____
Nearest tenth _____

5. 46.91
Nearest whole number _____
Nearest tenth _____

6. 56.83
Nearest whole number _____
Nearest tenth _____

7. 89.96
Nearest whole number _____
Nearest tenth _____

8. 32.17
Nearest whole number _____
Nearest tenth _____

9. 12.61
Nearest whole number _____
Nearest tenth _____

10. 59.98
Nearest whole number _____
Nearest tenth _____

I am learning to round decimals to the nearest whole number and the nearest tenth.

Round the number on each bird to the nearest whole number and the nearest tenth.

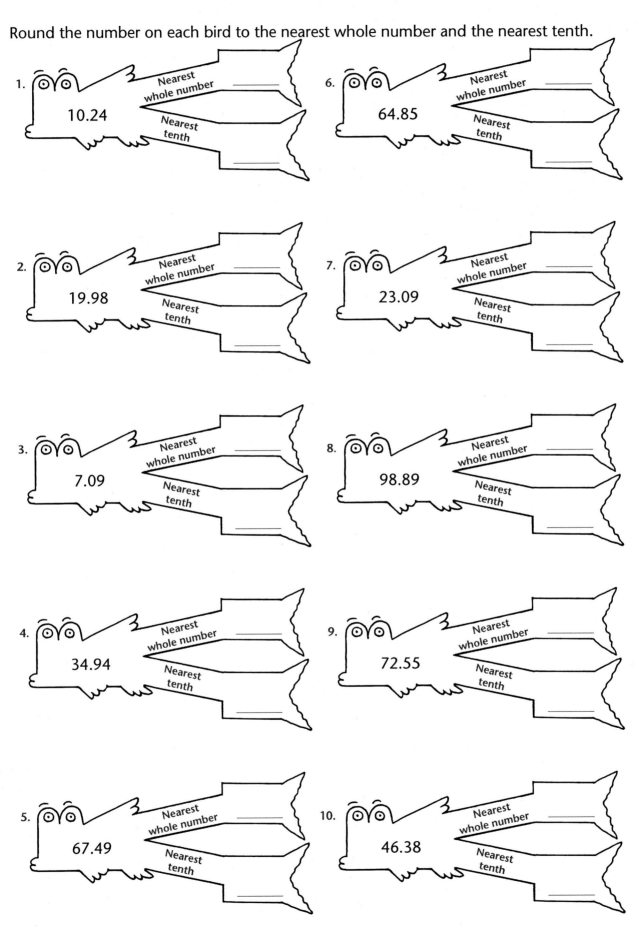

1. 10.24
Nearest whole number _____
Nearest tenth _____

2. 19.98
Nearest whole number _____
Nearest tenth _____

3. 7.09
Nearest whole number _____
Nearest tenth _____

4. 34.94
Nearest whole number _____
Nearest tenth _____

5. 67.49
Nearest whole number _____
Nearest tenth _____

6. 64.85
Nearest whole number _____
Nearest tenth _____

7. 23.09
Nearest whole number _____
Nearest tenth _____

8. 98.89
Nearest whole number _____
Nearest tenth _____

9. 72.55
Nearest whole number _____
Nearest tenth _____

10. 46.38
Nearest whole number _____
Nearest tenth _____

I am learning to:
- round decimals to the nearest whole number
- find the difference between the original and rounded numbers.

Add or subtract to make each number into the closest whole number. Write the number you have added or subtracted above the arrow. Write the whole number in the blank box. The first one is done for you.

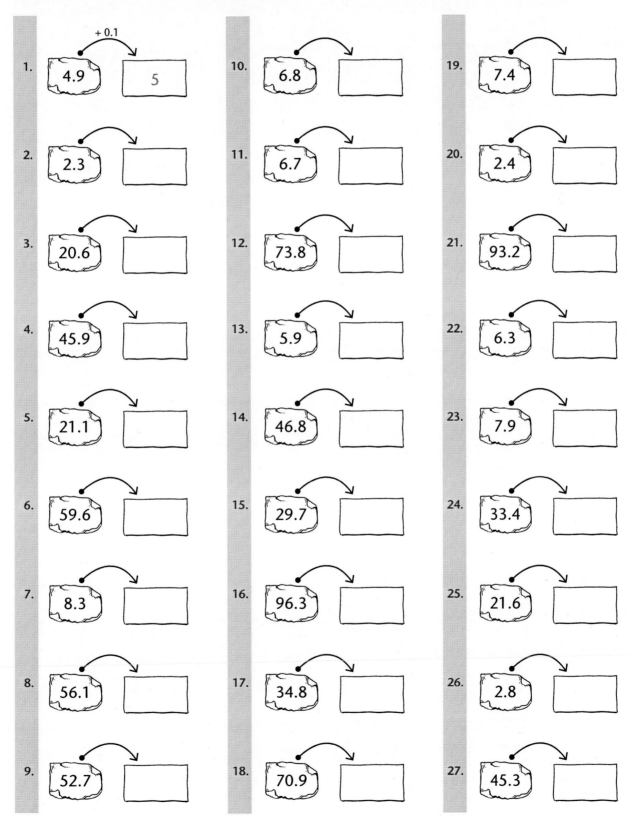

1. + 0.1   4.9 → 5

2. 2.3 →

3. 20.6 →

4. 45.9 →

5. 21.1 →

6. 59.6 →

7. 8.3 →

8. 56.1 →

9. 52.7 →

10. 6.8 →

11. 6.7 →

12. 73.8 →

13. 5.9 →

14. 46.8 →

15. 29.7 →

16. 96.3 →

17. 34.8 →

18. 70.9 →

19. 7.4 →

20. 2.4 →

21. 93.2 →

22. 6.3 →

23. 7.9 →

24. 33.4 →

25. 21.6 →

26. 2.8 →

27. 45.3 →

I am learning to:
- round decimals to the nearest whole number
- find the difference between the original and rounded numbers.

Add or subtract to make each number into the closest whole number. Write the number you have added or subtracted above the arrow. Write the whole number in the blank box. The first one is done for you.

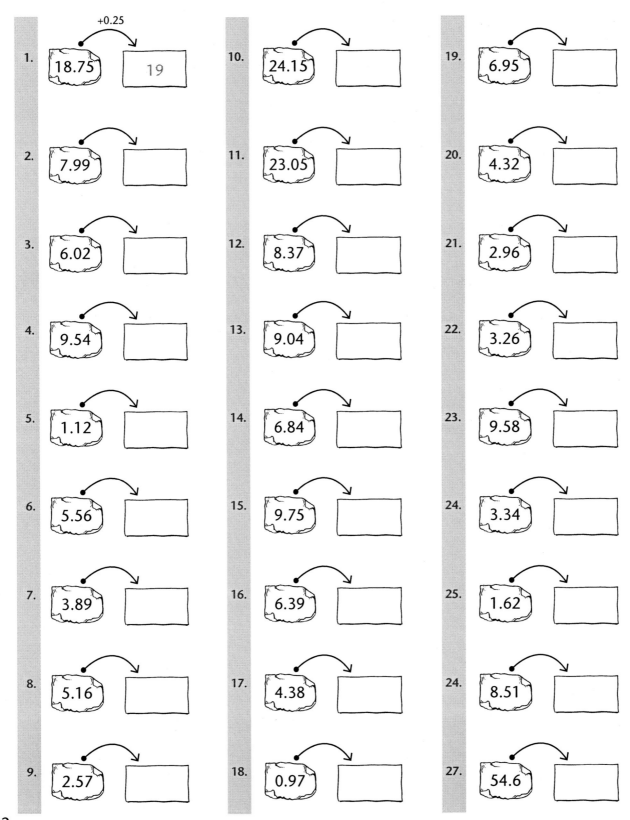

1. +0.25 18.75 → 19

2. 7.99 →

3. 6.02 →

4. 9.54 →

5. 1.12 →

6. 5.56 →

7. 3.89 →

8. 5.16 →

9. 2.57 →

10. 24.15 →

11. 23.05 →

12. 8.37 →

13. 9.04 →

14. 6.84 →

15. 9.75 →

16. 6.39 →

17. 4.38 →

18. 0.97 →

19. 6.95 →

20. 4.32 →

21. 2.96 →

22. 3.26 →

23. 9.58 →

24. 3.34 →

25. 1.62 →

24. 8.51 →

27. 54.6 →

Pupil template

Put some decimal numbers onto the untidy piece of paper and give the sheet to a partner to complete.

Add or subtract to make each number into the closest whole number. Write the number you have added or subtracted above the arrow. Write the whole number in the blank box. The first one is done for you.

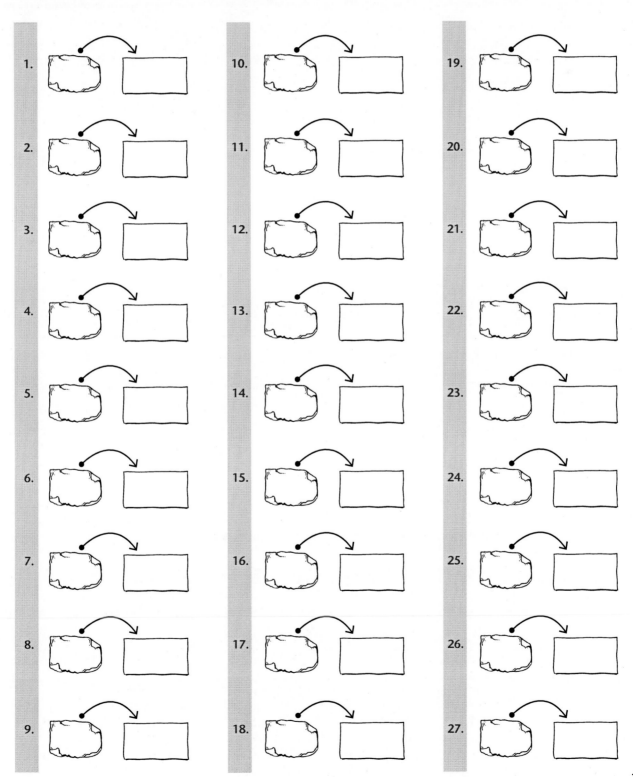

33

Developing strategies for adding decimal numbers

I am learning to use the numberline to solve decimal addition problems by bridging to whole numbers.

A. Complete each equation by placing the two numbers you are given on the numberline and jumping from the first number to a whole number and then to the answer. The first one is started for you.

1.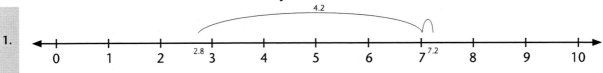

   2.8 + _____ = 7.2

2.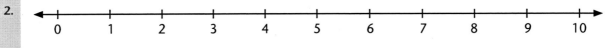

   5.7 + _____ = 9.4

3.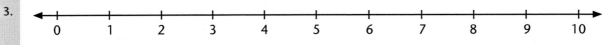

   3.9 + _____ = 8.1

4.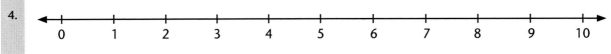

   2.8 + _____ = 7.3

5.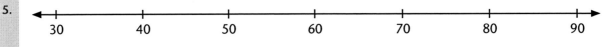

   49.88 + _____ = 72.4

6.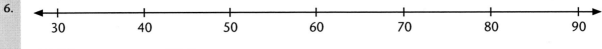

   69.95 + _____ = 92.6

7.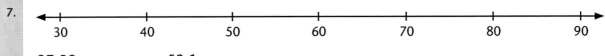

   27.99 + _____ = 53.1

8.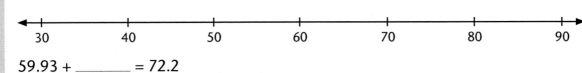

   59.93 + _____ = 72.2

B. Draw your own numberlines in your book and complete these problems.

1. 39.48 + _____ = 56.71   3. 49.62 + _____ = 87.5   5. 53.96 + _____ = 67.8

2. 67.21 + _____ = 89.5   4. 32.40 + _____ = 68.01   6. 46.72 + _____ = 75.39

34

© Essential Resources Educational Publishers Ltd, 2009

I am learning to use the numberline to solve decimal addition problems by bridging to whole numbers.

A. Complete each equation by placing the two numbers you are given on the numberline and jumping from the first number to a whole number and then to the answer. The first one is started for you.

1.
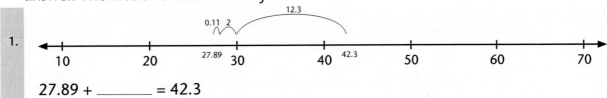

27.89 + _____ = 42.3

2.
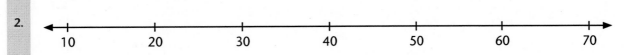

16.95 + _____ = 63.6

3.
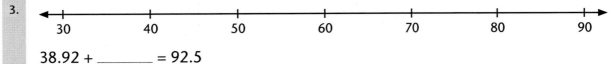

38.92 + _____ = 92.5

4.
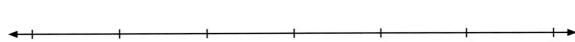

49.88 + _____ = 72.4

5.
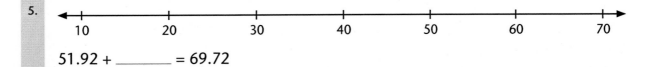

51.92 + _____ = 69.72

6.
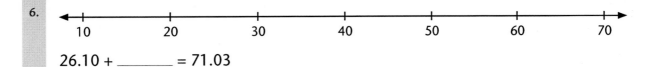

26.10 + _____ = 71.03

7.
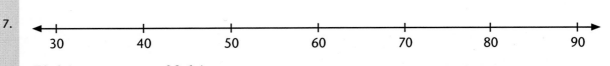

73.14 + _____ = 83.14

8.
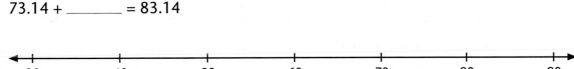

48.11 + _____ = 81.26

B. Draw your own numberlines in your book and complete these problems.

1. 32.81 + _____ = 64.28   3. 19.49 + _____ = 42.67   5. 46.74 + _____ = 66.74

2. 25.63 + _____ = 67.40   4. 52.82 + _____ = 63.21   6. 34.03 + _____ = 57.09

A. Solve each equation using the numberline. The first one is started for you.

1.

23.4

$23.4 + 36.3 =$ _____

2.

15.7

$15.7 + 18.1 =$ _____

3.

14.3

$14.3 + 57.6 =$ _____

4.

83.5

$83.5 + 23.1 =$ _____

5.

26.3

$26.3 + 31.4 =$ _____

6.

$94.2 + 61.7 =$ _____

7.

$33.56 + 12.12 =$ _____

8.

$45.48 + 58.31 =$ _____

B. Draw your own numberlines in your book and complete these problems.

1. $46.33 + 27.45 =$ ____	**3.** $96.42 + 3.63 =$ ____	**5.** $31.85 + 47.14 =$ ____
2. $81.59 + 10.53 =$ ____	**4.** $70.79 + 6.26 =$ ____	**6.** $18.41 + 58.37 =$ ____

I am learning to mentally add ones, tens, tenths, hundredths and thousandths separately when appropriate.

A. Solve each equation using the numberline.

1.

←———|————————————————————————|——→
    16.61

16.61 + 34.35 = _____

2.

←———|————————————————————————|——→
    38.38

38.38 + 63.41 = _____

3.

←———|————————————————————————|——→
    42.12

42.12 + 24.64 = _____

4.

←———|————————————————————————|——→
    76.43

76.43 + 19.43 = _____

5.

←———|————————————————————————|——→
    89.17

89.17 + 75.81 = _____

6.

←———|————————————————————————|——→

64.627 + 28.151 = _____

7.

←———|————————————————————————|——→

13.122 + 46.336 = _____

8.

←———|————————————————————————|——→

47.421 + 57.117 = _____

B. Draw your own numberlines in your book and complete these problems.

1. 74.167 + 23.632 = _____   **3.** 83.642 + 26.246 = _____

2. 53.267 + 45.632 = _____   **4.** 43.921 + 34.076 = _____

I am learning to solve addition problems when the two numbers are easily related to doubles.

A. Make each decimal into a whole number.

1.8		4.9		9.6		11.8		5.5	
13.8		8.7		6.6		9.1		7.2	

B. Use your number knowledge to work out these problems. Write your thoughts in the thought bubbles.

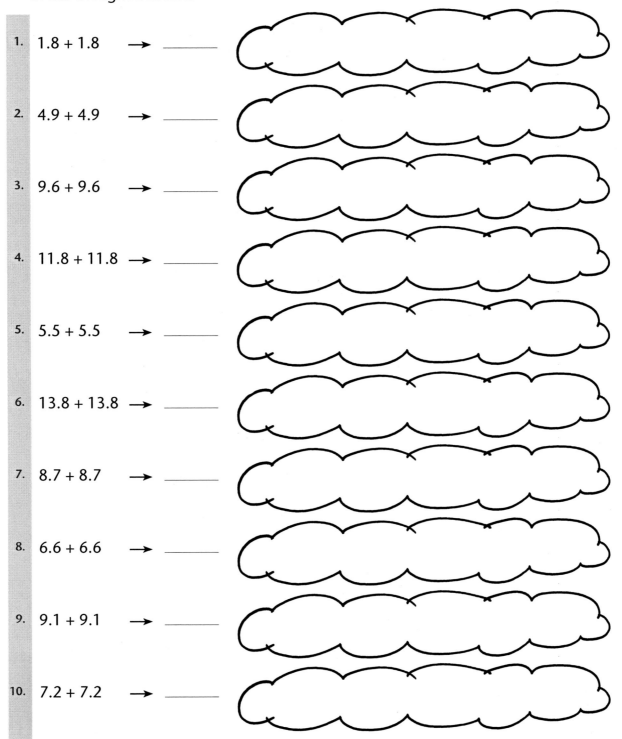

1. 1.8 + 1.8 → _____

2. 4.9 + 4.9 → _____

3. 9.6 + 9.6 → _____

4. 11.8 + 11.8 → _____

5. 5.5 + 5.5 → _____

6. 13.8 + 13.8 → _____

7. 8.7 + 8.7 → _____

8. 6.6 + 6.6 → _____

9. 9.1 + 9.1 → _____

10. 7.2 + 7.2 → _____

I am learning to solve addition problems when the two numbers are easily related to doubles.

A. Make each decimal into a whole whole number.

35.2		49.8		60.4		99.3		68.9	
31.9		77.7		59.5		44.9		98.2	

B. Use your number knowledge to work out these problems. Write your thoughts in the thought bubbles.

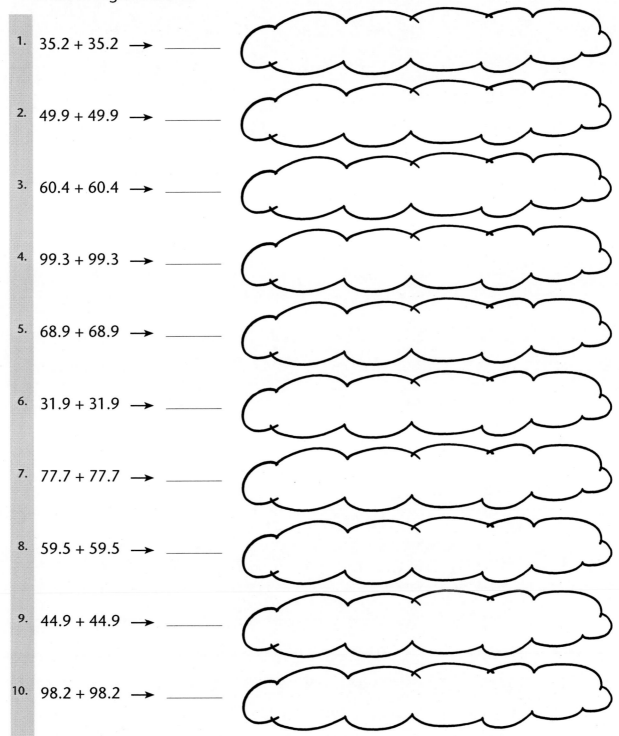

1. 35.2 + 35.2 → _____

2. 49.9 + 49.9 → _____

3. 60.4 + 60.4 → _____

4. 99.3 + 99.3 → _____

5. 68.9 + 68.9 → _____

6. 31.9 + 31.9 → _____

7. 77.7 + 77.7 → _____

8. 59.5 + 59.5 → _____

9. 44.9 + 44.9 → _____

10. 98.2 + 98.2 → _____

Developing strategies for subtracting decimal numbers

I am learning to solve subtraction problems by equal additions that turn one of the numbers into a whole number.

Solve each equation by turning one of the numbers into a whole number.

1. 55.1 – 39.8 ↓ ↓ 55 – 39.7 = ____	**8.** 23.4 – 19.9 ↓ ↓ ____ – ____ = ____	**15.** 79.9 – 28.4 ↓ ↓ ____ – ____ = ____
2. 69.8 – 32.3 ↓ ↓ ____ – ____ = ____	**9.** 89.3 – 2.8 ↓ ↓ ____ – ____ = ____	**16.** 81.2 – 19.8 ↓ ↓ ____ – ____ = ____
3. 41.2 – 9.7 ↓ ↓ ____ – ____ = ____	**10.** 49.6 – 17.2 ↓ ↓ ____ – ____ = ____	**17.** 63.1 – 39.4 ↓ ↓ ____ – ____ = ____
4. 43.4 – 19.7 ↓ ↓ ____ – ____ = ____	**11.** 79.5 – 27.7 ↓ ↓ ____ – ____ = ____	**18.** 45.8 – 19.9 ↓ ↓ ____ – ____ = ____
5. 85.3 – 49.5 ↓ ↓ ____ – ____ = ____	**12.** 73.6 – 29.7 ↓ ↓ ____ – ____ = ____	**19.** 63.2 – 49.8 ↓ ↓ ____ – ____ = ____
6. 72.3 – 47.9 ↓ ↓ ____ – ____ = ____	**13.** 68.2 – 17.8 ↓ ↓ ____ – ____ = ____	**20.** 84.4 – 27.9 ↓ ↓ ____ – ____ = ____
7. 53.9 – 27.8 ↓ ↓ ____ – ____ = ____	**14.** 91.2 – 58.6 ↓ ↓ ____ – ____ = ____	**21.** 63.4 – 17.8 ↓ ↓ ____ – ____ = ____

I am learning to solve subtraction problems by equal additions that turn one of the numbers into a whole number.

Solve each equation by turning one of the numbers into a whole number.

1. 55.4 – 28.6	↓　　↓ _____ – _____ = _____	**8.** 91.3 – 38.4	↓　　↓ _____ – _____ = _____	**15.** 83.5 – 48.8	↓　　↓ _____ – _____ = _____
2. 74.6 – 37.8	↓　　↓ _____ – _____ = _____	**9.** 84.1 – 58.2	↓　　↓ _____ – _____ = _____	**16.** 41.6 – 17.9	↓　　↓ _____ – _____ = _____
3. 83.4 – 48.2	↓　　↓ _____ – _____ = _____	**10.** 76.5 – 18.6	↓　　↓ _____ – _____ = _____	**17.** 67.8 – 19.4	↓　　↓ _____ – _____ = _____
4. 73.6 – 29.7	↓　　↓ _____ – _____ = _____	**11.** 63.2 – 49.8	↓　　↓ _____ – _____ = _____	**18.** 29.8 – 13.9	↓　　↓ _____ – _____ = _____
5. 84.3 – 69.5	↓　　↓ _____ – _____ = _____	**12.** 45.2 – 25.9	↓　　↓ _____ – _____ = _____	**19.** 87.2 – 56.8	↓　　↓ _____ – _____ = _____
6. 95.3 – 45.9	↓　　↓ _____ – _____ = _____	**13.** 87.2 – 39.8	↓　　↓ _____ – _____ = _____	**20.** 72.4 – 53.9	↓　　↓ _____ – _____ = _____
7. 73.9 – 47.8	↓　　↓ _____ – _____ = _____	**14.** 97.2 – 65.6	↓　　↓ _____ – _____ = _____	**21.** 78.4 – 49.8	↓　　↓ _____ – _____ = _____

I am learning to choose the best strategy to solve a problem.

Circle the strategy you would choose to solve the problem. Justify your choice and then solve the problem.

	Problem	Strategy	Justification	Answer
1.	23.4 + 36.3	Place value Compensation Near doubles		
2.	47.421 + 57.117	Place value Compensation Near doubles		
3.	59.5 + 59.5	Place value Compensation Near doubles		
4.	39.48 + 36.37	Place value Compensation Near doubles		
5.	41.2 – 9.7	Place value Compensation Near doubles		
6.	69.95 + 72.8	Place value Compensation Near doubles		
7.	94.2 + 61.7	Place value Compensation Near doubles		
8.	95.3 – 45.9	Place value Compensation Near doubles		
9.	68.9 + 68.9	Place value Compensation Near doubles		

I am learning to choose the best strategy to solve a problem.

Write some equations to go into the problem column and give to a partner to complete.

Circle the strategy you would choose to solve the problem. Justify your choice and then solve the problem.

	Problem	Strategy	Justification	Answer
1.		Place value Compensation Near doubles		
2.		Place value Compensation Near doubles		
3.		Place value Compensation Near doubles		
4.		Place value Compensation Near doubles		
5.		Place value Compensation Near doubles		
6.		Place value Compensation Near doubles		
7.		Place value Compensation Near doubles		
8.		Place value Compensation Near doubles		

Using averaging and multiplication for adding whole numbers

I am learning to solve addition problems using averaging and multiplication.

A. Use averaging to solve these cherry problems.

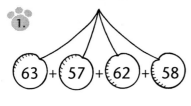

1. $63 + 57 + 62 + 58$

_____ × _____ = _____

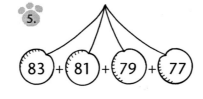

5. $83 + 81 + 79 + 77$

_____ × _____ = _____

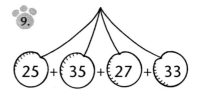

9. $25 + 35 + 27 + 33$

_____ × _____ = _____

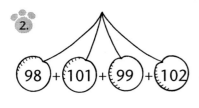

2. $98 + 101 + 99 + 102$

_____ × _____ = _____

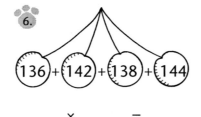

6. $136 + 142 + 138 + 144$

_____ × _____ = _____

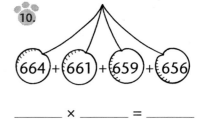

10. $664 + 661 + 659 + 656$

_____ × _____ = _____

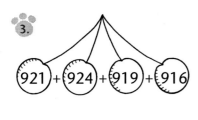

3. $921 + 924 + 919 + 916$

_____ × _____ = _____

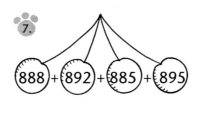

7. $888 + 892 + 885 + 895$

_____ × _____ = _____

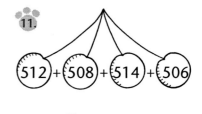

11. $512 + 508 + 514 + 506$

_____ × _____ = _____

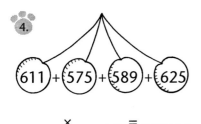

4. $611 + 575 + 589 + 625$

_____ × _____ = _____

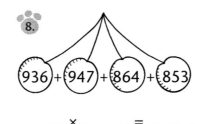

8. $936 + 947 + 864 + 853$

_____ × _____ = _____

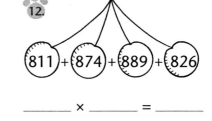

12. $811 + 874 + 889 + 826$

_____ × _____ = _____

B. Make up some cherry problems for your partner to solve.

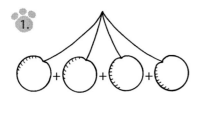

1. ◯ + ◯ + ◯ + ◯

_____ × _____ = _____

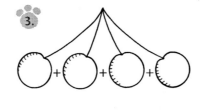

3. ◯ + ◯ + ◯ + ◯

_____ × _____ = _____

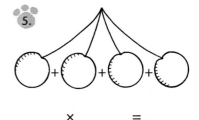

5. ◯ + ◯ + ◯ + ◯

_____ × _____ = _____

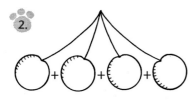

2. ◯ + ◯ + ◯ + ◯

_____ × _____ = _____

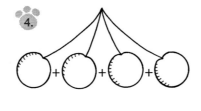

4. ◯ + ◯ + ◯ + ◯

_____ × _____ = _____

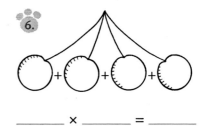

6. ◯ + ◯ + ◯ + ◯

_____ × _____ = _____

44

© Essential Resources Educational Publishers Ltd, 2009

Using averaging and division for subtracting whole numbers

I am learning to solve subtraction problems where common factors can be found.

A. For each of these problems find a common factor to help you make an easier equation to solve. The first one is started for you.

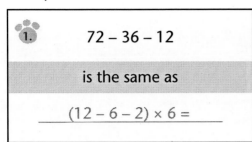
1.   72 – 36 – 12

is the same as

_____ (12 – 6 – 2) × 6 = _____

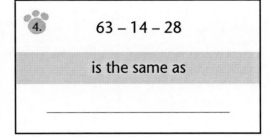
4.   63 – 14 – 28

is the same as

_____

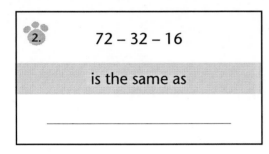
2.   72 – 32 – 16

is the same as

_____

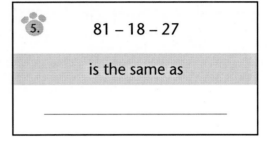
5.   81 – 18 – 27

is the same as

_____

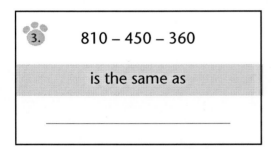
3.   810 – 450 – 360

is the same as

_____

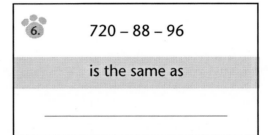
6.   720 – 88 – 96

is the same as

_____

B. Join the boxes that have common factors that will help you make the equation easier to solve.

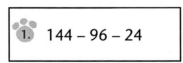
1. 144 – 96 – 24

a. (40 – 8 – 11) × 8   →

2. 180 – 36 – 45

b. (50 – 15 – 5) × 7   →

3. 320 – 64 – 88

c. (12 – 8 – 2) × 12   →

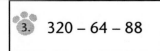
4. 350 – 105 – 35

d. (20 – 4 – 5) × 9   →

I am learning to solve subtraction problems using averaging and division.

A. For each of these problems find a common factor to help you make an easier equation to solve. The first one is started for you.

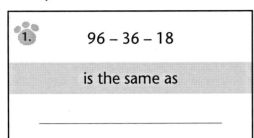

1.

96 – 36 – 18

is the same as

_____

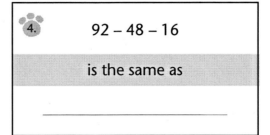

4.

92 – 48 – 16

is the same as

_____

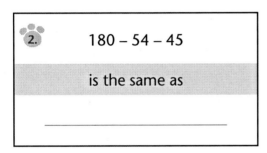

2.

180 – 54 – 45

is the same as

_____

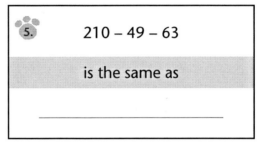

5.

210 – 49 – 63

is the same as

_____

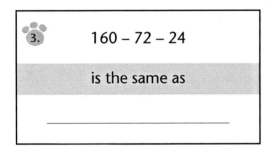

3.

160 – 72 – 24

is the same as

_____

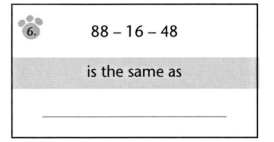

6.

88 – 16 – 48

is the same as

_____

B. Join the boxes that have common factors that will help you make the equation easier to solve.

1. 270 – 63 – 81

a. (20 – 9 – 3) × 6 →

2. 120 – 54 – 18

b. (90 – 70 – 6) × 8 →

3. 630 – 350 – 140

c. (30 – 7 – 9) × 9 →

4. 720 – 560 – 48

d. (90 – 50 – 20) × 7 →

I am learning to order _____

Order these _____

 1

_____

 2.

_____

 3.

_____

 4.

_____

 5.

_____

I am learning to _____

Fill in the missing numbers on the numberline.

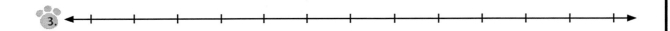

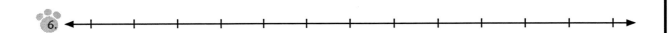

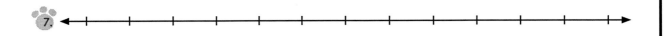

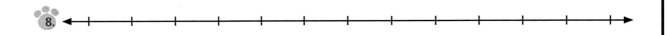

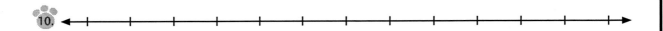

I am learning to _____

Fill in the missing numbers.

I am learning to _____

I am learning to _____

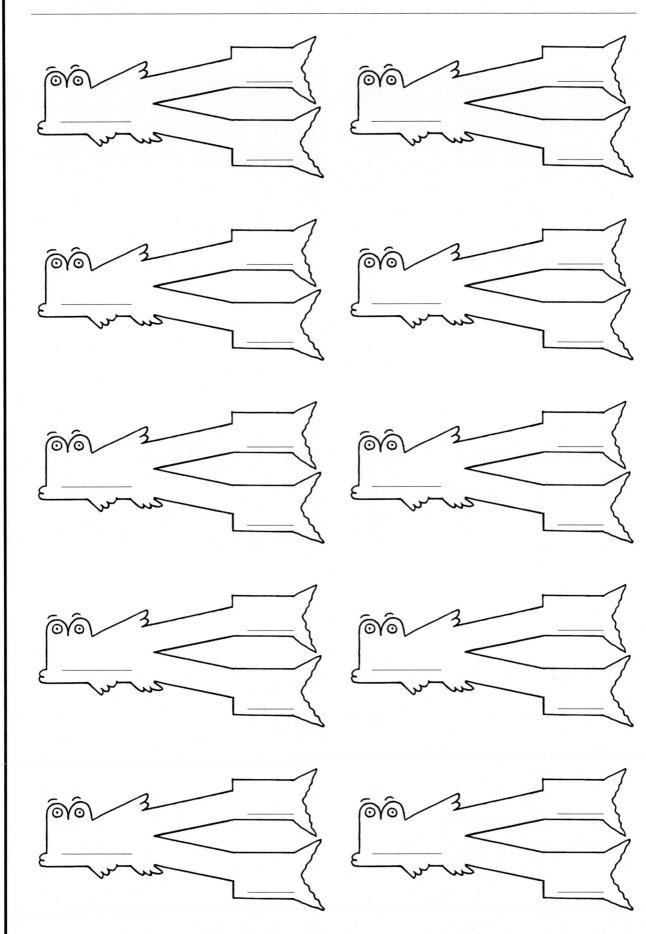

Answers to activity sheets

Page 5

1.	27.712	27.722	27.732
	27.742	27.752	
2.	1.919	1.929	1.939
	1.949	1.959	1.969
3.	89.393	89.403	89.413
	89.423	89.433	89.443
4.	61.204	61.214	61.224
	61.234	61.244	61.254
5.	2.43	2.44	2.45
	2.46	2.47	2.48
6.	17.615	17.625	17.635
	17.645	17.655	17.665
7.	46.28	46.29	46.30
	46.31	46.32	46.33
8.	38.526	38.536	38.546
	38.556	38.566	38.576

Page 6

1.	65.652	65.642	65.632
	65.622	65.612	
2.	78.285	78.275	78.265
	78.255	78.245	78.235
3.	12.053	12.043	12.033
	12.023	12.013	12.003
4.	47.453	47.443	47.433
	47.423	47.413	47.403
5.	83.581	83.571	83.561
	83.551	83.541	83.531
6.	36.052	36.042	36.032
	36.022	36.012	36.002
7.	57.529	57.519	57.509
	57.499	57.489	57.479
8.	92.736	92.726	92.716
	92.706	92.696	92.686

Page 7

1.	16.862	16.863	16.864
	16.865	16.866	
2.	63.307	63.308	63.309
	63.310	63.311	63.312
3.	98.792	98.793	98.794
	98.795	98.796	98.797
4.	31.944	31.945	31.946
	31.947	31.948	31.949
5.	57.460	57.461	57.462
	57.463	57.464	57.465
6.	84.619	84.620	84.621
	84.622	84.623	84.624

Page 7 continued

7.	52.176	52.177	52.178
	52.179	52.180	52.181
8.	40.528	40.529	40.530
	40.531	40.532	40.533

Page 8

1.	45.136	45.135	45.134
	45.133	45.132	
2.	37.424	37.423	37.422
	37.421	37.420	37.419
3.	90.703	90.702	90.701
	90.700	90.699	90.698
4.	78.658	78.657	78.656
	78.655	78.654	78.653
5.	82.341	82.340	82.339
	82.338	82.337	82.336
6.	23.688	23.687	23.686
	23.685	23.684	23.683
7.	64.562	64.561	64.560
	64.559	64.558	64.557
8.	56.875	56.874	56.873
	56.872	56.871	56.870

Page 9

1. $\frac{1}{4}\ \frac{2}{4}\ \frac{3}{4}\ \frac{4}{4}\ \frac{5}{4}\ \frac{6}{4}\ \frac{7}{4}\ \frac{8}{4}\ \frac{9}{4}\ \frac{10}{4}\ \frac{11}{4}\ \frac{12}{4}$

2. $\frac{1}{3}\ \frac{2}{3}\ \frac{3}{3}\ \frac{4}{3}\ \frac{5}{3}\ \frac{6}{3}\ \frac{7}{3}\ \frac{8}{3}\ \frac{9}{3}\ \frac{10}{3}\ \frac{11}{3}\ \frac{12}{3}$

3. $\frac{1}{2}\ \frac{2}{2}\ \frac{3}{2}\ \frac{4}{2}\ \frac{5}{2}\ \frac{6}{2}\ \frac{7}{2}\ \frac{8}{2}\ \frac{9}{2}\ \frac{10}{2}\ \frac{11}{2}\ \frac{12}{2}$

4. $\frac{1}{5}\ \frac{2}{5}\ \frac{3}{5}\ \frac{4}{5}\ \frac{5}{5}\ \frac{6}{5}\ \frac{7}{5}\ \frac{8}{5}\ \frac{9}{5}\ \frac{10}{5}\ \frac{11}{5}\ \frac{12}{5}$

5. $\frac{1}{6}\ \frac{2}{6}\ \frac{3}{6}\ \frac{4}{6}\ \frac{5}{6}\ \frac{6}{6}\ \frac{7}{6}\ \frac{8}{6}\ \frac{9}{6}\ \frac{10}{6}\ \frac{11}{6}\ \frac{12}{6}$

6. $\frac{1}{8}\ \frac{2}{8}\ \frac{3}{8}\ \frac{4}{8}\ \frac{5}{8}\ \frac{6}{8}\ \frac{7}{8}\ \frac{8}{8}\ \frac{9}{8}\ \frac{10}{8}\ \frac{11}{8}\ \frac{12}{8}$

7. $\frac{1}{9}\ \frac{2}{9}\ \frac{3}{9}\ \frac{4}{9}\ \frac{5}{9}\ \frac{6}{9}\ \frac{7}{9}\ \frac{8}{9}\ \frac{9}{9}\ \frac{10}{9}\ \frac{11}{9}\ \frac{12}{9}$

8. $\frac{1}{7}\ \frac{2}{7}\ \frac{3}{7}\ \frac{4}{7}\ \frac{5}{7}\ \frac{6}{7}\ \frac{7}{7}\ \frac{8}{7}\ \frac{9}{7}\ \frac{10}{7}\ \frac{11}{7}\ \frac{12}{7}$

9. $\frac{4}{5}\ \frac{5}{5}\ \frac{6}{5}\ \frac{7}{5}\ \frac{8}{5}\ \frac{9}{5}\ \frac{10}{5}\ \frac{11}{5}\ \frac{12}{5}\ \frac{13}{5}\ \frac{14}{5}\ \frac{15}{5}\ \frac{16}{5}$

10. $\frac{1}{10}\ \frac{2}{10}\ \frac{3}{10}\ \frac{4}{10}\ \frac{5}{10}\ \frac{6}{10}\ \frac{7}{10}\ \frac{8}{10}\ \frac{9}{10}\ \frac{10}{10}\ \frac{11}{10}\ \frac{12}{10}$

Page 10

1.	4.251	7.894	7.984
	8.967	8.976	9.876
2.	6.279	6.927	7.629
	7.962	9.726	9.762
3.	5.562	5.625	5.652
	6.225	6.252	6.552
4.	89.654	89.899	89.989
	90.989	91.899	99.891
5.	62.347	62.734	67.234
	67.432	76.347	76.734

Page 11

1.	39.620	39.602	39.260
	39.062	38.206	38.026
2.	8.410	8.401	7.140
	7.104	7.041	7.014
3.	14.975	14.957	14.795
	14.759	14.597	14.579
4.	8.833	8.803	8.383
	8.338	8.308	8.083
5.	26.541	26.514	26.451
	26.415	26.154	26.145

Page 12 Position of coloured segment may vary

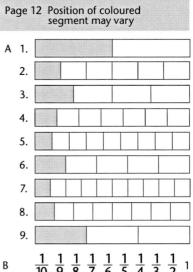

A
1.
2.
3.
4.
5.
6.
7.
8.
9.

B $\frac{1}{10}\ \frac{1}{9}\ \frac{1}{8}\ \frac{1}{7}\ \frac{1}{6}\ \frac{1}{5}\ \frac{1}{4}\ \frac{1}{3}\ \frac{1}{2}\ 1$

Rules will vary.

Page 13

2. 9 thousandths
3. 1 tenth
4. 3 thousandths
5. 4 tenths
6. 3 ones
7. 1 hundredth
8. 7 tenths
9. 7 tenths
10. 4 hundredths
11. 8 hundredths
12. 3 thousandths
13. 7 hundredths
14. 3 tenths
15. 6 tenths
16. 5 ones
17. 1 hundredth
18. 1 thousandth
19. 1 one
20. 2 tenths
21. 5 thousandths
22. 2 tenths
23. 2 hundredths
24. 5 hundredths

Page 14

A1.	600	D1.	0.08
2.	0.06	2.	0.8
3.	6	3.	0.08
4.	0.006	4.	8
5.	60	5.	800
B1.	0.05	6.	0.08
2.	5	7.	0.8
3.	0.5	8.	0.08
4.	500	9.	8
5.	0.005	10.	800
C1.	0.7	E1.	ones
2.	0.007	2.	thousands
3.	7	3.	thousands
4.	0.007	4.	hundred thousands
5.	700		

F, G, H. Answers will vary

Page 15

2. 1 + 0.2 + 0.06 + 0.003
3. 4 + 0.1 + 0.07 + 0.002
4. 7 + 0.5 + 0.09 + 0.007
5. 5 + 0.2 + 0.07 + 0.004
6. 2 + 0.4 + 0.01 + 0.008
7. 6 + 0.08 + 0.003
8. 7 + 0.3 + 0.02 + 0.001
9. 6 + 0.8 + 0.02 + 0.006
10. 9 + 0.4 + 0.01 + 0.005
11. 1 + 0.1 + 0.05
12. 3 + 0.9 + 0.006
13. 5 + 0.06 + 0.004
14. 2 + 0.5 + 0.09 + 0.009
15. 4 + 0.7 + 0.03 + 0.008
16. 8 + 0.3 + 0.08 + 0.005

Page 16

2.	8	0.8	0.00	0.002
3.	4	0.5	0.06	0.008
4.	3	0.1	0.01	0.004
5.	7	0.9	0.08	0.002
6.	4	0.6	0.07	0.001
7.	9	0.2	0.00	0.005
8.	6	0.0	0.07	0.003
9.	5	0.1	0.06	0.006
10.	1	0.3	0.02	0.004
11.	4	0.7	0.08	0.009
12.	6	0.1	0.05	0.007
13.	1	0.4	0.09	0.009
14.	6	0.2	0.03	0.006
15.	3	0.8	0.04	0.008
16.	5	0.5	0.01	0.005
17.	7	0.3	0.03	0.009
18.	5	0.9	0.04	0.006
19.	2	0.6	0.02	0.000
20.	8	0.4	0.05	0.008
21.	1	0.0	0.02	0.001
22.	9	0.7	0.01	0.007
23.	4	0.2	0.09	0.004
24.	6	0.9	0.00	0.005

Page 17

A1.	26.539	C2.	89.279
2.	19.982	3.	42.954
3.	87.904	4.	27.003
4.	36.565	5.	48.357
5.	74.068	6.	11.704
6.	36.692	7.	70.949
7.	21.507	8.	65.8
8.	85.192	9.	21.616
9.	66.073	10.	37.852
10.	54.195	11.	68.457
B1.	4.689		
2.	8.904		
3.	3.563		
4.	7.085		
5.	5.34		

Page 18

2. 100 + 6 + 0.05 + 0.001
3. 90 + 1 + 0.7 + 0.04 + 0.003
4. 800 + 90 + 8 + 0.5 + 0.04 + 0.004
5. 70 + 2 + 0.1 + 0.005
6. 80 + 0.6 + 0.03 + 0.008
7. 100 + 20 + 2 + 0.4 + 0.09 + 0.007
8. 100 + 1 + 0.5 + 0.009
9. 10 + 5 + 0.3 + 0.01 + 0.003
10. 300 + 80 + 3 + 0.08 + 0.009
11. 400 + 70 + 0.9 + 0.09 + 0.006
12. 20 + 9 + 0.2 + 0.07 + 0.001
13. 900 + 40 + 2 + 0.3 + 0.02 + 0.003
14. 40 + 7 + 0.8 + 0.02 + 0.008
15. 30 + 4 + 0.08 + 0.002
16. 50 + 3 + 0.1 + 0.07 + 0.004
17. 40 + 8 + 0.7 + 0.06 + 0.007
18. 60 + 5 + 0.6 + 0.05 + 0.002
19. 50 + 9 + 0.2 + 0.08 + 0.006
20. 70 + 4 + 0.8 + 0.03 + 0.004
21. 60 + 6 + 0.9 + 0.05 + 0.001
22. 100 + 10 + 7 + 0.4 + 0.06 + 0.002
23. 60 + 5 + 0.2 + 0.09 + 0.007
24. 1 + 0.2 + 0.06 + 0.007
25. 800 + 70 + 9 + 0.3 + 0.04 + 0.006

Page 19

A1.	37 220	3 722	372
2.	8 475	847	84
3.	4 939	493	49
4.	178 632	17 863	1 786
5.	2 505	250	25
6.	2 384	238	23
7.	60 167	6 016	601
8.	5 698	569	56
9.	194 067	19 406	1 940
10.	54 832	5 483	548

B1.	485 697	4.	19 879
2.	148 371	5.	73 962
3.	36 949	6.	281 376

Page 20

A1.	5 496	549	54
2.	36 578	3 657	365
3.	45 879	4 587	458
4.	12 315	1 231	123
5.	72 020	7 202	720
6.	83 245	8 324	832
7.	496 209	49 620	4 962
8.	453 928	45 392	4 539
9.	623 074	62 307	6 230
10.	814 602	81 460	8 146

B1.	434 683	4.	3 724 556
2.	824 986	5.	1 694 268
3.	763 542	6.	745 291

Page 21

2. $\frac{7}{3}$ $2\frac{1}{3}$

3. $\frac{12}{6}$ 2

4. $\frac{19}{10}$ $1\frac{9}{10}$

5. $\frac{5}{2}$ $2\frac{1}{2}$

6. $\frac{12}{5}$ $2\frac{2}{5}$

7. $\frac{12}{8}$ $1\frac{1}{2}$

8. $\frac{5}{3}$ $1\frac{2}{3}$

Page 22

1. $\frac{4}{2}$ 2

2. $\frac{15}{8}$ $1\frac{7}{8}$

3. $\frac{6}{5}$ $1\frac{1}{5}$

4. $\frac{8}{3}$ $2\frac{2}{3}$

5. $\frac{4}{3}$ $1\frac{1}{3}$

6. $\frac{12}{10}$ $1\frac{2}{10}$ or $1\frac{1}{5}$

7. $\frac{8}{5}$ $1\frac{3}{5}$

8. $\frac{11}{4}$ $2\frac{3}{4}$

Page 24

1. red: $\frac{3}{5}$ $\frac{12}{20}$ $\frac{30}{50}$ $\frac{300}{500}$ $\frac{15}{25}$ $\frac{6}{10}$ $\frac{9}{15}$

2. green: $\frac{1}{2}$ $\frac{500}{1000}$ $\frac{3}{6}$ $\frac{50}{100}$ $\frac{5}{10}$ $\frac{4}{8}$ $\frac{10}{20}$

3. purple: $\frac{3}{4}$ $\frac{6}{8}$ $\frac{9}{12}$ $\frac{30}{40}$ $\frac{300}{400}$ $\frac{12}{16}$ $\frac{15}{20}$

4. orange: $\frac{8}{10}$ $\frac{4}{5}$ $\frac{80}{100}$ $\frac{40}{50}$ $\frac{16}{20}$ $\frac{24}{30}$ $\frac{32}{40}$

5. yellow: $\frac{2}{3}$ $\frac{4}{6}$ $\frac{6}{9}$ $\frac{8}{12}$ $\frac{10}{15}$ $\frac{20}{30}$ $\frac{200}{300}$

Page 25

1. red: $\frac{1}{2}$ $\frac{4}{8}$ $\frac{5}{10}$ $\frac{10}{20}$ $\frac{25}{50}$ $\frac{50}{100}$ $\frac{500}{1000}$

2. green: $\frac{1}{10}$ $\frac{2}{20}$ $\frac{3}{30}$ $\frac{10}{100}$ $\frac{50}{500}$ $\frac{100}{1000}$

3. purple: $\frac{2}{5}$ $\frac{40}{100}$ $\frac{6}{15}$ $\frac{400}{1000}$ $\frac{20}{50}$ $\frac{40}{100}$ $\frac{4}{10}$

4. orange: $\frac{1}{5}$ $\frac{6}{30}$ $\frac{5}{25}$ $\frac{10}{50}$ $\frac{20}{100}$ $\frac{200}{1000}$

5. yellow: $\frac{1}{4}$ $\frac{10}{40}$ $\frac{2}{8}$ $\frac{100}{400}$ $\frac{25}{100}$ $\frac{5}{20}$ $\frac{50}{200}$

6. blue: $\frac{3}{4}$ $\frac{300}{400}$ $\frac{12}{16}$ $\frac{750}{1000}$ $\frac{15}{20}$ $\frac{75}{100}$ $\frac{30}{40}$

7. brown $\frac{3}{5}$ $\frac{12}{20}$ $\frac{30}{50}$ $\frac{60}{100}$ $\frac{300}{500}$ $\frac{6}{10}$ $\frac{600}{1000}$

Page 26

1.	$\frac{1}{2}$ $\frac{4}{8}$	3.	$1\frac{8}{8}$	5.	$\frac{2}{5}$ $\frac{8}{20}$
2.	$\frac{2}{3}$ $\frac{4}{6}$	4.	$\frac{3}{4}$ $\frac{15}{20}$	6.	$\frac{5}{6}$ $\frac{10}{12}$

Page 27

1.	4	11.	40	21.	49
2.	28	12.	85	22.	10
3.	30	13.	3	23.	25
4.	17	14.	9	24.	8
5.	59	15.	6	25.	6
6.	73	16.	13	26.	3
7.	69	17.	7	27.	23
8.	135	18.	6	28.	6
9.	29	19.	15	29.	8
10.	58	20.	8	30.	10

Page 28

1.	16.1	11.	50	21.	59.5
2.	54.2	12.	91.6	22.	64.8
3.	65.8	13.	69.8	23.	72.7
4.	49.1	14.	16.2	24.	85.7
5.	72.4	15.	27.2	25.	72.4
6.	31.7	16.	54.3	26.	72.9
7.	36.0	17.	63.8	27.	65.6
8.	21.2	18.	73.0	28.	55.0
9.	69.3	19.	96.9	29.	71.0
10.	91.5	20.	61.7	30.	83.3

Page 29

1.	88, 87.7	6.	57, 56.8
2.	31, 31.1	7.	90, 90
3.	30, 29.8	8.	32, 32.2
4.	84, 83.7	9.	13, 12.6
5.	47, 46.9	10.	60, 60

Page 30

1.	10, 10.2	6.	65, 64.9
2.	20, 20	7.	23, 23.1
3.	7, 7.1	8.	99, 98.9
4.	35, 34.9	9.	73, 72.6
5.	67, 67.5	10.	46, 46.4

Page 31

1.	5	10.	7	19.	7
2.	2	11.	7	20.	2
3.	21	12.	74	21.	93
4.	46	13.	6	22.	6
5.	21	14.	47	23.	8
6.	60	15.	30	24.	33
7.	8	16.	96	25.	22
8.	56	17.	35	26.	3
9.	53	18.	71	27.	45

© Essential Resources Educational Publishers Ltd, 2009

Page 32

1.	19	10.	24	19.	7
2.	8	11.	23	20.	4
3.	6	12.	8	21.	3
4.	10	13.	9	22.	3
5.	1	14.	7	23.	10
6.	6	15.	10	24.	3
7.	4	16.	6	25.	2
8.	5	17.	4	26.	9
9.	3	18.	1	27.	55

Page 34

A1.	4.4	B1.	17.23
2.	3.7	2.	22.29
3.	4.2	3.	37.88
4.	4.5	4.	35.61
5.	22.52	5.	13.84
6.	22.65	6.	28.67
7.	25.11		
8.	12.27		

Page 35

A1.	14.41	B1.	31.47
2.	46.65	2.	41.77
3.	53.58	3.	23.18
4.	22.52	4.	10.39
5.	17.8	5.	20
6.	44.93	6.	23.06
7.	10		
8.	33.15		

Page 36

A1.	59.7	B1.	73.78
2.	33.8	2.	92.12
3.	71.9	3.	100.05
4.	106.6	4.	77.05
5.	57.7	5.	78.99
6.	155.9	6.	76.78
7.	45.68		
8.	103.79		

Page 37

A1.	50.96	B1.	97.799
2.	101.79	2.	98.899
3.	66.76	3.	109.888
4.	95.86	4.	77.997
5.	164.98		
6.	92.778		
7.	59.458		
8.	104.538		

Page 38

A.	2, 5, 10, 12, 6, 14, 9, 7, 9, 7		
B1.	3.6	6.	27.6
2.	9.8	7.	17.4
3.	19.2	8.	13.2
4.	23.6	9.	18.2
5.	11	10.	14.4

Page 39

A.	35, 50, 60, 99, 69, 32, 78, 60, 45, 98		
B1.	70.4	6.	63.8
2.	99.8	7.	155.4
3.	120.8	8.	119
4.	198.6	9.	89.8
5.	137.8	10.	196.4

Page 40

1.	15.3	8.	3.5	15.	51.5
2.	37.5	9.	86.5	16.	61.4
3.	31.5	10.	32.4	17.	23.7
4.	23.7	11.	51.8	18.	25.9
5.	35.8	12.	43.9	19.	13.4
6.	24.4	13.	50.4	20.	56.5
7.	26.1	14.	32.6	21.	45.6

Page 41

1.	26.8	8.	52.9	15.	34.7
2.	36.8	9.	25.9	16.	23.7
3.	35.2	10.	57.9	17.	48.4
4.	43.9	11.	13.4	18.	15.9
5.	14.8	12.	19.3	19.	30.4
6.	49.4	13.	47.4	20.	18.5
7.	26.1	14.	31.6	21.	28.6

Page 42

1.	59.7	6.	142.75
2.	104.538	7.	155.9
3.	119	8.	49.4
4.	75.85	9.	137.8
5.	31.5		

Page 44

1.	240	7.	3 560
2.	400	8.	3 600
3.	3 680	9.	120
4.	2 400	10.	2 640
5.	320	11.	2 040
6.	560	12.	3 400

Page 45

A1.	24	B1.	c, 24
2.	24	2.	d, 99
3.	0	3.	a, 168
4.	21	4.	b, 210
5.	36		
6.	536		

Page 46

A1.	42	B1.	c, 126
2.	81	2.	a, 48
3.	64	3.	d, 140
4.	28	4.	b, 112
5.	98		
6.	24		